Retold by Kathryn Smith
Illustrated by Stuart Trotter
Religious consultant: Meryl Doney
Language consultant: Betty Root

This is a Parragon Publishing book
This edition published in 2005

Parragon Publishing
Queen Street House
4 Queen Street
BATH BA1 1HE, UK

Printed in Indonesia

David
and
Goliath

p

Long ago there was a young boy called David, who had seven older brothers. David's brothers were big and strong.

They had work to do, and they didn't
have much time for their little brother.
David sometimes felt small and unimportant.
"I wish I was big and strong, too,"
he sighed. "Then I could help."

One day, David's father gave him a job of his own.

"I need a shepherd to take care of my sheep," he told him. "You must lead them to food and water. You must scare away wild animals with this sling and stones. And you must count the sheep every day, to make sure they are all safe!"

David was very excited to be given such an important job. He told God all about it. "It will be hard work," he told God. "But I know you will be there to help me."

PING!

David spoke to God every day, asking questions and learning from Him.

Of course, it was very quiet up in the hills, with just the sheep for company. Sometimes David didn't see another person all day. But whenever he felt lonely, David got out his harp and made up songs, to remind himself that God was near.

He kept busy, too, doing target practice with his sling. Soon, he never missed a target.

PING! With just one stone, David could scare away even the fiercest lions and wolves!

While David was learning to be a good shepherd, his three biggest brothers had joined the Israelite army, led by King Saul.

The Israelite army was away fighting the army of the Philistines. But they weren't doing very well. The Philistine army had a secret weapon—a giant soldier called Goliath.

Goliath was much taller than the other men. He carried the longest spear the Israelites had ever seen.

He was as **strong** as a bear,

as **fierce** as a wolf,

and as **brave** as a lion.

One morning, David's father sent him to take food to his brothers. And what a surprise he got when he arrived. Goliath was standing in the middle of the battlefield, shaking his spear at the Israelites.

"Listen!" he roared. "Send your best soldier to fight me. If he wins, we will be your slaves. If I win, you will be ours."

David's big brothers hid behind their shields and began to tremble.

"Who is brave enough to fight that giant?" they cried.

Then David stepped forward. "I will fight him," he said bravely.

His brothers stared in disbelief. **"YOU!"** they laughed. "How can a little boy like you fight a giant?"

"I may be little," replied David, "but with God's help, I can do big things."

Try as they might, the brothers could not change David's mind. So they took him to see King Saul.

King Saul couldn't believe his ears when he heard what David wanted to do. "You're just a shepherd boy!" he exclaimed. "Goliath will cut you into little pieces!"

David smiled. "God helped me protect my sheep, and he will help me fight Goliath, too. Please let me try."

At last the King agreed. "Wear my armor to protect yourself," he offered. But David shook his head.

"It's much too **big**" he replied. "God will be my armor."

THUD! THUD! THUD! The ground shook as Goliath stepped forward to fight. "Where is your champion?" he roared, shaking his fist.

"Here I am!" yelled David, shouting up at the giant.

"HO! HO! HO! HA! HA! HA!" Goliath
guffawed with laughter.
"That's a good joke! They've sent
a boy to fight me."

HA! HA! HA!

The Israelites began to shiver and shake with fear. This was a stupid idea! Why did they ever think David could fight Goliath?

But David was not afraid. "Goliath is right!" he cried. "I am just a boy. But I have God with me. He helped me fight wild bears and lions. And He will help me fight Goliath, too."

All of a sudden, David didn't seem so funny anymore. Goliath shook his fist and gave an almighty roar. "Israelites, prepare to become our slaves!"

Very quietly, David took a smooth stone from his pouch.
Very calmly, he loaded it into his sling.
Very carefully, he took aim.
David spun the sling around his head. PING!
Before Goliath had even raised his spear, the stone flew
out of the sling and struck him— THUMP!—right in
the middle of his forehead.

WHIZZ! WHIZZ! WHIZZ!

PING!

CRASH! Goliath fell to the ground in a heap of armor. David had won the battle. For a moment there was silence. Then a huge cheer went up.

David's brothers cheered. The other Israelite soldiers cheered. Even King Saul cheered.

"Hooray!" they all cried. "Hooray for David the giant-slayer!"

After the battle, King Saul took David back to his palace. Everyone cheered for David the giant-killer!
That was the very first battle that David won.
But it wasn't the last. He grew up to be a great soldier, and even became king of Israel when Saul died.

But no matter how important David became, he never forgot the lesson he had learned—that, with God's help, even the smallest person can do big things!